# Family Ins and Outs

## Susan Wallace

Living Social Studies:
A Canadian Social Studies and
Supplementary Reading Program
for the Primary Grades

Toronto
Oxford University Press
1985

**Canadian Cataloguing in Publication Data**

Wallace, Susan, 1942–
    Family ins and outs

(Living social studies)
For use in elementary schools.
ISBN 0-19-540481-5

1. Family - Juvenile literature.   2. Parents -
Juvenile literature.   I. Title.   II. Series.

HQ734.W33 1985       306.8       C85-098044-5

This book is dedicated
to a man I have never met,
Bill Martin Jr.,
who said,
"Hopefully the day will come when books,
at least for elementary children,
will have considerable material
printed in spoken language patterns,"
and to my children
Tracy and Douglas
who claim they have helped
to write all my stories and are
demanding a share of any royalties
which may accrue.

"A Picnic" (text only) from *Up the Windy Hill* by Aileen
Fisher and published by Abelard Press, 1953. Copyright ©
renewed 1981. Reprinted by permission of Aileen Fisher.

*Eat*, story and illustration by Diane Paterson, copyright ©
1975 by Diane Paterson. Reprinted by permission of the
publisher, Dial Books For Young Readers, a Division of E. P.
Dutton, Inc.

*Editorial/Production*  Patrick Trant, Elspeth Staniland,
                        Ruth Hanley

*Covers/Design*  Bob Paul

ISBN 0 19 540481 5

Printed in Canada by Friesen Printers
1 2 3 4 5 6 7 8 9 — 94 93 92 91 90 89 88 87 86 85

# Table of Contents

# A Parent Can

story:   Susan Wallace
pictures:   Karen Giffin

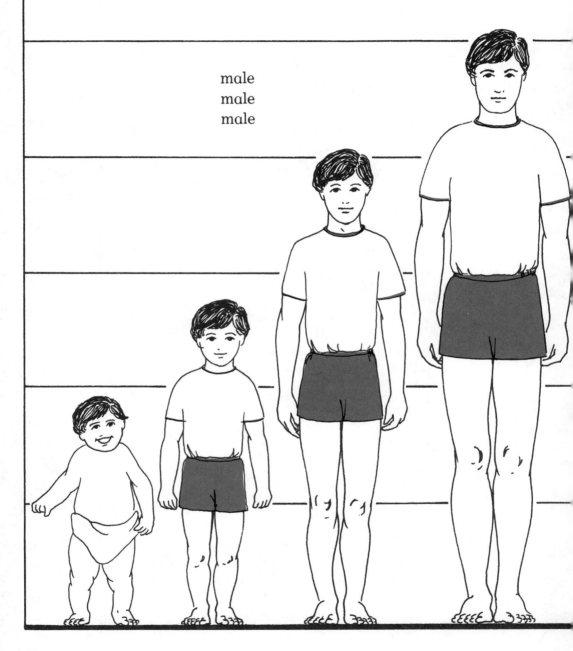

male
male
male

If you were born a boy,

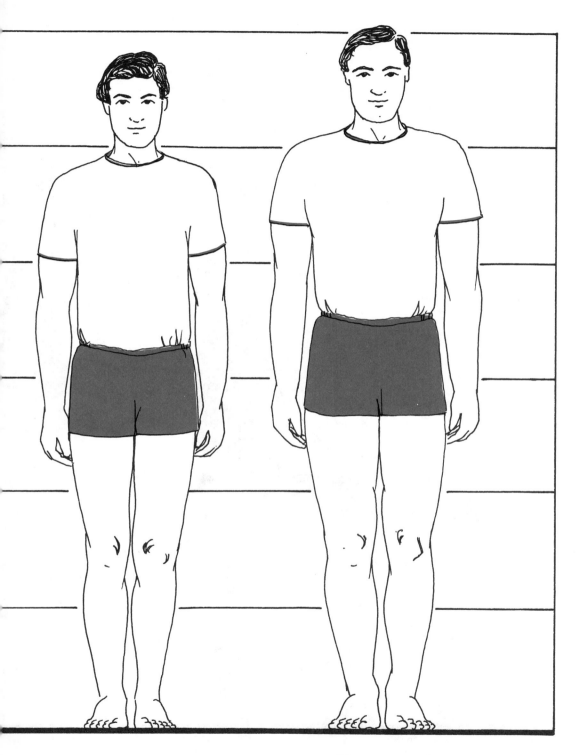

you will grow up to be a man.
You have no choice.

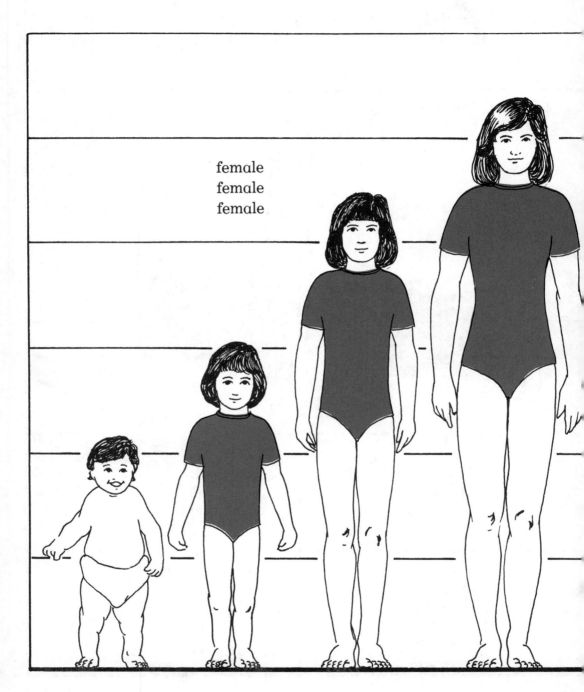

female
female
female

If you were born a girl,

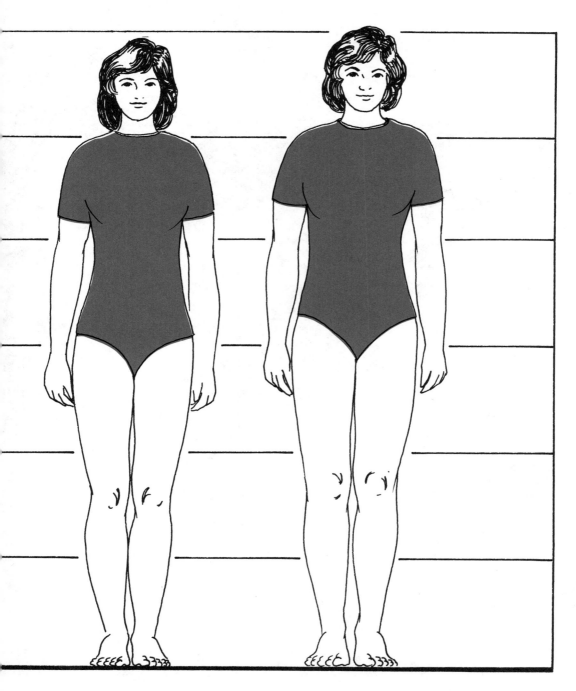

you will grow up to be a woman.
You have no choice.

But you can choose
to be a parent.

# Being A Parent

story:   Susan Wallace
pictures:   Karen Giffin

Being a parent is not easy.
Sometimes it's not even fun -
Cooking and cleaning and scolding,
Always work to be done.

Being a parent is not easy,
But sometimes it can be fun -
Picnics and hotdogs and hugging,
A *family* day in the sun.

A parent can...

make beds

change
the
baby

cook

vacuum

read a s

cut the
grass

sing

eed the dog

clean

paint the
house

kiss

hug

play ball

go to work

11

# Wash The Dishes

*traditional rhyme*
*picture:   Pierre Doré*

Wash the dishes.
  Dry the dishes.
    Turn the dishes over.

Wash the dishes.
  Dry the dishes.
    Turn the dishes over.

Wash the dishes.
  Dry the dishes.
    Turn the dishes over.

# A Picnic

*poem:   Aileen Fisher*
*pictures:   Kim Herbener*

We had a picnic.
We had buns.
We had wieners -
big, fat ones.

We had wieners
on a stick...
Mother told us:
"Don't be quick,

turn your wieners
front and back,
cook them slowly
till they crack."

We
had
cookies
and
lemonade.

Beth saw
a bee
and got afraid.

15

I dropped a pickle
in the dirt,

but I washed it off
so it didn't hurt.

We had a picnic.
Was it fun!

**Now** all we want
is another one!

# Grandpa

*story:* Susan Wallace
*pictures:* Pierre Doré

Grandpa,
  Grandpa,
    Grandpa,

don't sleep
in your chair.

Grandpa,
 Grandpa,
  Grandpa,

 let's go out
   somewhere...

somewhere...

somewhere...

19

# My Daddy Is My Daddy

story: Susan Wallace
pictures: Helen Fox

"I would like you,"
said Kevin,
"to meet my Daddy."

He is like a bear:
full of strength,
but cuddly and warm and brown.

He is like a lion,
romping and playing
with his cubs.

But *look out* if he hears you have...

been rude to Mommy...

not done your work at school...

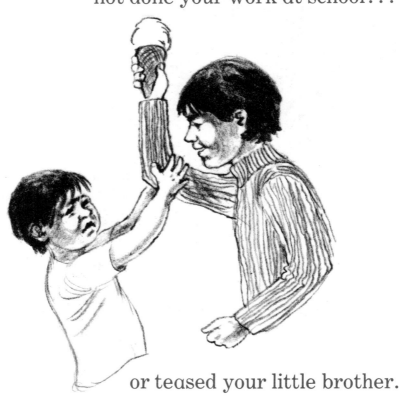

or teased your little brother.

He can **roar so loud**

that
everything shakes,

and you get sent right
to your room.

"My daddy doesn't often roar,"
said Kevin.

More often, he is like a magician.

He works his magic
              and,

                        suddenly...

my record player
is fixed...

I find quarters
behind my ears...

and I can ride
a two-wheeled bike
all by myself.

On Saturday morning,
when I open my eyes
and remember
it is Saturday,
I think of my Daddy.

27

As Saturday gets going,

> and the cars start moving
> up and down
> my street,

I follow them
with my eyes.
I think of my Daddy.

Then . . .

Daddy comes.

He always comes

*swinging*

into our driveway
in his big, blue car.

I run down the driveway
to meet him.

He takes my hand,
and we walk
together.

"So how's my
big boy?"
he asks.

And he listens,
and he listens,
and he listens.

"Nobody can listen
quite like my Daddy,"
said Kevin.

# Stories About Mothers

*stories and pictures:*
*Grade 1 Children,*
*Silvercreek School,*
*Mississauga, Ontario*

A Mother is

someone who gives

you a name

I'll call her kirsty

By Kirsty

A Mother is someone who hates it when you don't want to eat dinner and you make faces

by Farzana

A Mother is someone who makes you feel you are the best child in the world by Greg

A Mother is someone who gets
you dressed up nicely when
you are going to a party.
by Debjani

A Mother is someone who
takes you to Beavers
when it's your first time
going there
by Adam

A Mother is someone who changes my baby sister's diapers and take care of us. by Chris Lucenti.

A Mother is someone who makes you laugh by Stephanie

A Mother is someone
who is there when
you get hurt on your
skateboard

by Adrienne

My Mother can play the piano.
She plays in a band.

A Mother is a person too. by Mike

STORY AND PICTURES BY DIANE PATERSON

This is Martha.

This is her father,

and this is her mother.

Martha would not eat.

Mother and Father cooked

special things for her.

45

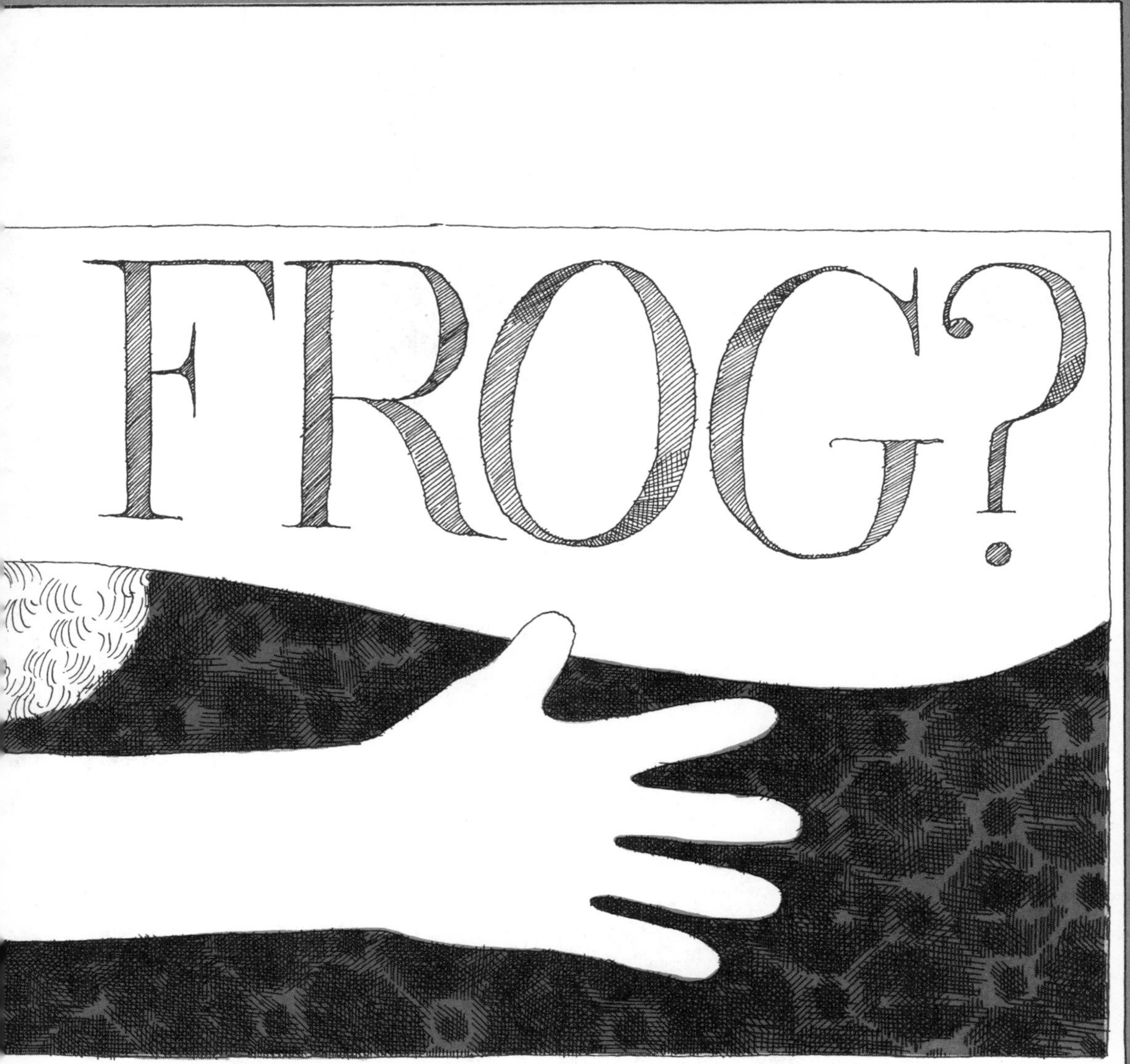
FROG?

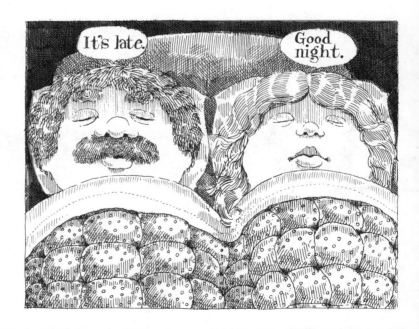

# We Wish You . . .

*traditional songs*
*pictures:   Kim Herbener*

HERBENER

We wish you a Merry Christmas,
   We wish you a Merry Christmas,
We wish you a Merry Christmas,
   And a Happy New Year.

We wish you a happy Chanukah,
We wish you a happy Chanukah,
We wish you a happy Chanukah,
And a Happy Jewish New Year...

Happy Chinese New Year to you,
Happy Indian New Year to you,
Happy New Year, dear children.
Happy New Year to you.